Seriously, SNOW WHITE WAS SO FORGETFUL!

The Story of

SNOW WHITE DWARVES

as Told by THE

by Na... ...rlais

Raintree is an imprint of Capstone Global Library Limited,
a company incorporated in England and Wales having its
registered office at 7 Pilgrim Street, London, EC4V 6LB –
Registered company number: 6695582

To contact Raintree, please email myorders@raintreepublishers.co.uk.

First published by Picture Window Books © 2013
First published in the United Kingdom in 2013
The moral rights of the proprietor have been asserted.

Editors: Laura Knowles and Jill Kalz
Art Director: Nathan Gassman
Designer: Lori Bye
Production Specialist: Jennifer Walker
Originated by Capstone Global Library Ltd
Printed and bound in China by Leo Paper Products Ltd

The illustrations in this book were created digitally.

Special thanks to our adviser, Terry Flaherty, PhD, Professor of English,
Minnesota State University, Mankato, for his expertise.

ISBN 978 1 406 26664 1 (paperback)
17 16 15 14 13
10 9 8 7 6 5 4 3 2 1

British Library Cataloguing in Publication Data
A full catalogue record for this book is available from the British Library.

I love Snow White dearly. She's a beautiful person, inside and out.

But honestly, the girl's got a mind like a leaky bucket.

Here's the REAL story of Snow White and the Seven Dwarves. (My name, by the way, is Seven. We dwarves used to have real names, but Snow White couldn't remember them.)

One day, we came home from the mines to find our cottage door open. We thought we'd been burgled! But no. It was just a lovely little girl, sound asleep.

4

In the morning she had quite a story to tell.

"Hello!" she said. "I'm Snow White. The queen sent me into the woods, and a hunter was supposed to kill me, but he was nice and let me go, and I wandered a long time in the woods. I guess I'm very pretty, and that's why the queen doesn't like me. I'm Snow White. Would it be all right if I lived with you? I love playing house, and doing real housework wouldn't be all that different, would it? Did I tell you my name is Snow White?"

Wow, did she have energy.

Life with Snow White was... interesting. She'd forget to turn on the oven. She'd forget to turn it *off*.

She'd make banana cream pie and forget the bananas.

She'd knit scarves that were 10 metres long – just because she forgot to stop.

On the bright side, she laughed at all of our jokes. And she never complained about anything.

Years passed. Snow White grew up, but
she didn't really change. She remained her
sweet, charming, forgetful self.

Then one day, Five heard a rumour.

"The queen knows Snow White is alive!" he told us.
"The magic mirror spilled the beans!"

We gave Snow White orders to stay inside the cottage. She was not to open the door to anyone. We knew the evil queen would try to hurt her.

But Snow White quickly forgot.
Twice we came home to find her
lying on the floor. It was clearly
the work of the queen.

The first time,
Snow White couldn't
breathe. She was wearing
a brand-new corset that
was laced too tightly.

The second time she had a poisoned comb in her hair.

All the queen had to do was dress up as an old woman and
offer something pretty for sale. Any thoughts of being
careful went right out of Snow White's head!

We posted reminders. We even wrote

DO NOT OPEN THE DOOR

in syrup on her pancakes.

But once again we came home to find Snow White
on the floor. This time we couldn't help her. There was
no corset to loosen or comb to remove. We thought
she was dead, killed by a magical spell. And yet, days
passed, and she remained as lovely as ever.

"It's like she's forgotten how to wake up,"

Five whispered.

We couldn't make ourselves bury her. So we placed Snow White in a glass coffin and brought her to a spot on the mountainside. We took turns guarding her.

Thank goodness, that's not the end of the story!

Suddenly I was face-to-face with a prince! But he barely noticed me. He couldn't take his eyes off Snow White.

"What happened to her?" he asked. "What's her name?"

I told him the whole story.

"She's the most beautiful girl I've ever seen," he breathed. "Those lips, those eyes! What did you say her name was? Could I take her with me? Now that I've seen her, I don't think I can live without her! What silky hair she has! Tell me again, what's her name?"

I smiled. The prince reminded me of a certain someone.

We were bringing Snow White back to the cottage, so the other dwarves could say goodbye. Without warning the prince stopped and turned around. "Hey, what about lunch?" he asked.

The servants slipped.

The coffin slid.

And Snow White coughed.

I'd never heard such a beautiful sound. Out of her throat flew a bit of rosy red apple. Rosy red POISONED apple, that is.

She sat up. **"Did someone say something about lunch?"** she asked.

Yes, Snow White married the prince, of course.

The queen actually showed up at the reception, if you can believe it. Everyone threw bread rolls at her and booed so loudly that she ran away and was never heard from again.

21

Things are pretty much back to normal now. When it gets cold outside, we're grateful for our 10-metre scarves. And every once in a while, we make banana cream pie without any bananas. Just for old times' sake.

Think about it

Fairy tales have been around a long time and often have many different versions. What version of *Snow White and the Seven Dwarves* do you know best? How is it different from this one? How is it the same?

Who would you rather be friends with: someone who makes a lot of mistakes but is easy to get along with, or someone who does things well but points out all the things you do wrong?

The narrator in this story doesn't have a real name. Would you have felt differently about him if he'd had a name? How about if he were named One, or Four, or any of the other numbers?

How do you think the story would be different if it was told from the queen's point of view? How about the prince's point of view?

Glossary

narrator person who tells a story
point of view way of looking at something
version account of something from a certain point of view

Find out more

Books

Mixed Up Fairy Tales, Hilary Robinson, illustrated by Nick Sharratt (Hodder, 2005).

The Orchard Book of Hans Christian Andersen's Fairy Tales, Martin Waddell (Orchard, 2010).

Usborne Illustrated Grimm's Fairy Tales, Ruth Brockelhurst and Gillian Doherty (Usborne, 2012).

Website

storynory.com/archives/fairy-tales
Visit this website to listen to some of the best-loved fairy tales.

Other books in the series

Believe Me, Goldilocks Rocks!	978 1 406 24309 3
Honestly, Red Riding Hood Was Rotten!	978 1 406 24310 9
No Lie, I Acted Like a Beast!	978 1 406 26663 4
Seriously, Cinderella Is So Annoying!	978 1 406 24311 6
Trust Me, Jack's Beanstalk Stinks!	978 1 406 24312 3